MW00852489

HOW I BECAME A MERMAID

AMANDA ALCÁNTARA

www.amandaalcantara.com
contact@amandaalcantara.com

Cover art and design:
Eddaviel
www.mentesextremofilas.com

Illustration on page 67:
Franchesca Santiago Sosa

Author headshot on page 86:
Yelaine Rodriguez

ISBN-13: 978-0-578-29445-2

howibecameamermaid.info

To Hancy,
you gave us so much

Table of Contents

Content warning: This book contains mention and descriptions of suicide and self-harm that may be disturbing to some readers.

If you're struggling with suicidal thoughts, please call the U.S. national hotline: 1-800-273-8255.

Organizations offering affordable therapy (updated in 2022):
openpathcollective.org (in the U.S.)
1-849-638-2044 (en la República Dominicana)

"Hippolyta lights her CIGARETTE with a candle. Notes the darkness in her eyes. That *je ne sais quoi* that makes her *the* Josephine Baker is gone.

HIPPOLYTA

You got that look again.

Josephine takes a deep drag, before –

JOSEPHINE BAKER

Nights like these, I burn so bright,
I feel like a star...

HIPPOLYTA

You are a star.

JOSEPHINE BAKER

NO, Cherie. Not like a movie star.
Anyone can be that. Me, I feel like
the stars in the black of space.
Magnificent, ancient. And already
extinguished."

- Misha Green, Lovecraft Country. 2019. Episode #107. misha-writes.com

The day I died, I dug myself out of my chest after it had swallowed me whole.

I was in Cabarete beach. It was one of those afternoons where the sky was purple as the sun set. And everything felt soft soft soft.

Sunsets feel like the time of the day when nothing else matters but knowing we all came here to die.

I was like 6 or 7 when I found out we all die. I was playing at a friend's house. We, the little kids, were talking about Selena's death. And one of the older kids approached us and let us know "we all die." We fought with him. "That's not true," I said.

I understood death to happen because of accidents or murder. I didn't know we were all heading there.

We went and asked one of the adults if it was true. I remember the person's face, a blank stare. I wonder now if it was hard for that person to tell us the truth. "Yes, it's true."

"Who told you that?" she asked. We pointed to the older kid.

Was it her responsibility to lie? Maybe, spare us the truth, give us time before the innocence faded away?

Is it my responsibility to keep the character in this book alive? To keep myself alive?

But maybe, what if, there is joy in dying?

Again. I was in Cabarete beach. On the side where the kite surfers are. It was a chilly January afternoon, even for Caribbean weather.

And I was writing a letter to you, my child. You, my legacy. You, my words. You, my future. Our future. That I was now transforming.

I was writing you telling you that I didn't die.

But that I was protecting you
Sparing you
By instead
becoming something non-human. Because that's what so much of the hole in my chest that kept eating me felt like. Humanity taken. Sunk. What is humanity if not the knowledge that
your mother loves you?

The ocean loves me. And so I became one of hers.

Supposedly people who have abandonment issues have this emptiness in their chest. Dique it could lead to some mental health issues. We eat everyone that wants to come into our lives.

I chose to eat myself instead. Over and over.

I stood up from my blanket. Left everything behind. The ocean seemed to call me. Like a soft whispered chorus with the voice of thousands of ancestors. Is this what the mermaid call sounds like? Is this why it's so captivating? Is this what traps the men lost at sea? Not a woman. But the past. Deep in its sunken blueness. My blues wrapping me. In their grip, in their cries, in their cracked soulful voices. Release release release. I just wanted release. From this body. And its hole in its chest. Is this what they felt when they jumped? Is this what they felt when they drowned? How dare I compare my silly blues to theirs?

I was here because of those who stayed and suffered and witnessed.

I walked and walked and walked into the sea's song. Into the thousand voices. With their tails and fins and fangs and vibrations. That's what we're all made of. Vibrations.

I walked into the ocean. The air slowly leaving my pores so that I could sink, even while the salt water tried to keep me afloat, something took hold of my arm. And dragged me in.

I wonder, for how long did they search for my body?

Soy Amanda, hija de Carmen y Marcos, descendiente de los Alcantara de San Juan de La Maguana, de los Ramirez de Laguna Prieta, de los Herrera de Santiago de los Caballeros, de los Burgos de Licey. Tatataranieta del General Victoriano Alcantara y del mason cubano José Herreras que se enamoró de una dominicana y dijo "aquí me quedo."

Soy descendiente de mujeres que no se complacen con el primero que se las lleve de la casa. Mujeres agricultoras y yerberas con nombres como Dolores y Consuelo—una reflexión del mundo al que entran, y de la medicina que traen. Mujeres que deciden su rumbo y se auto-definen como les da la gana, y dicen: de hoy en adelante llámame Amapola. Y así, sus verdaderos nombres permanecerán un misterio lejos de los malos hechizos.

Soy de una tierra llena de contradicciones. Donde la esclavitud primero llegó al nuevo mundo, y donde America nació, marcándola con una herencia de vergüenza y a la vez resistencia pura que no se ve en libros pero sí se escucha en las lenguas sueltas que no se retractan de decir la vaina, como es. Lenguas que viven burlá del sistema y atrapadas en él.

Soy de una tierra donde el patriotismo une al pueblo pero ofusca la igualdad. Donde la identidad es sobre ser gente alegre pero con un miedo—un peso en el pecho de que se rompa el fino hilo que sostiene esa identidad, agarrándose más de la amplitud de lo que no somos, que de lo que sí somos: gente que terminó naciendo en este pedazo de isla ilegítima sin nombre propio y que hizo de su realidad familias donde dar pelas es tan común como lo es sobarle la herida a un niño y con cariño decirle "eso es pa crecer." Porque de cada herida, hacemos algo concreto, de cada miseria, una salve.

One day, the pain was too much. It drowned my lungs in tears and mucus, it rippled through my skin and planted a seed in my hair that strangled my thoughts, wrapping them in shame. That night, I cut my hair off and yet the branches were back within days.

I started wearing make up to cover the sadness of my eyes and focus it on my luscious red lips, and tight clothes on my wild curves. Sometimes the pain looked like a man, ripe with fresh skin and sweat drops on the top of his lips like morning dew.

I hugged him between my legs and his brokenness fed my own. Even as i begged him to help with my burden, aren't cis men the so-called stronger gender, able to lift weights equivalent to more than my own frail body? Why then must my burden be heavier than his?

And so when he leaves, i rip his roots out from inside of me, leaving me empty with only his weeds while he bears the proud war scars of my nails on his back, saying "yea I fucked her."

Over time my skin became blue, like punching from within.

And yet it didn't start from within, it started when i was born and my skin didn't match the bright hospital lights and my tiny fingers tried to claw themselves back in.

My mouth too big, i screamed that i was alive and they heard me in the hospital and in the room next door and in the subway across the hudson river into the city where i am today. And around the entire block and at the american dream mall that would open 29 years later, and in the year 1968 when my grandpa left to puerto rico then the bronx then brooklyn then west new york and in the year 1912 during the dominican civil war where the feared coronel ampayé uttered his last words and was shot dead breaking a spell that protected him after fathering dozens of babies, one being Casimira who had to raise her kids with strong fists, they said she was dura like her dad. Her daughter María would be widowed and poor with 9 kids including my dad, and they all only owned one pair of shoes for school. and Maria's boys would grow up to love to lick little girl's feet, sticking their tongue between their toes and becoming kings of their hoods and royalty of their apartment complexes from pueblo nuevo to the bronx.

And it was heard in the mouth of the black Eve* in the land of hispaniola, who danced with her former slave master when the formerly enslaved were freed and he wrote about the incident complaining at her splendor, sweating with rage, saying “fuck these people,” and he and so many other white creoles fled to cuba.

and we, we don’t know her words.

So we can only imagine what they would be.

In the year 2052, i will have a granddaughter with a big mouth too, she will be the heir of my fortune made of pink sweat drops and a machete made of words that for so long i held as my only will.

And this is as much her story as it is mine.

First I had to survive. Not only survive, but thrive. I was to give this seed more than I had been granted. A story. A rescued lineage.

Remember where u came from mi niña. I came from things that don’t exist yet.

**Character after black Eve as told in Silvio Torres-Saillant’s “Introduction to Dominican Blackness”*

everything I do I want you to know I do it for you. and it sounds cursi to say that cuz of that song—I swear the moment anything becomes too big, too commercial, too advertised, it loses its power, even if the words are actually powerful. that happened with the Black Lives Matter movement—even Nike put out a whole pro Black campaign, exploiting factory workers on the other side of the globe. capitalism is a fucking plague.

I'm currently tryna birth you. Or your mom. I was asking male friends for sperm but decided to wait cuz u deserve a dad, or a second mom, a two parent home.

anyway. I want to write you and in that way give you life now like my own beloved Frankenstein. I want to imagine a future where you are free of this shit.

And poof like magic, it's done. You exist. Hello querida :)

for me to get free, I had to surrender to becoming one of the dozens of creatures we fear.

I became a mermaid.

When the attack that led to my transformation started, it felt like a dozen bricks fell on me. I actually wanted the bricks to be true and wanted nothing more than to die. as I write this story, I've been having nightmares of that time when this man became obsessed with me. He started with texts. Then phone calls. I had to file police reports. I had to change my number. Eventually. I even moved away from the town where I lived.

but. Over the years. I knew he was still there, like a pot of water over a very low fire, just waiting for a reaction from me to raise the temp on the entire thing and make the water boil and spill over.

that's how these online attacks felt. something I couldn't escape or respond to, something I couldn't be saved from and a problem so big, police were useless, therapists were empty-handed, and loved ones had no idea how to react. They didn't know what to say. the reactions went from concern (not comforting), to straight up gaslighting like shit was my fault.

I mean maybe it was my fault.

once, when I was a kid, two boys from the neighborhood who I used to play with threatened to suddenly rape me. it came out of nowhere. I would be left alone at home during the day and they would come over to play. But it's like they learned they had dicks or something and figured out what it was for and they assumed I had to submit to it.

I ran inside my house when they tried to jump me. Before I could shut the door, they stuck a broom stick in between the wall and the door so I couldn't close it. Finally, the younger one noticed I was crying. And he pulled the stick out so I could close the door and lock myself inside.

I was sobbing. terrified. I called Mami at work to tell her what had happened. she didn't know who the boys were so I lied and told her they were teens. though they were 9 and I was 10. But I knew I had to lie.

I already knew at that age, I wouldn't be taken seriously if I said they were younger. It didn't matter that it was two of them. It didn't matter that they were stronger.

my mom called all the neighbors to warn them.

And we sort of just forgot the whole thing. but my body remembers that day, that fear.

My dominicanidad eats mangos over the sink and wears white on sundays
My dominicanidad loves to show off my perfect spanish and pretend I never left santiago
My dominicanidad steps into the room and everyone turns
My dominicanidad remembers las sirenas criollas are thick so I dont need to lose weight
My dominicanidad admires the brown freckles on my face like my most favorite inheritance

My dominicanidad hates wearing red white and blue
It pretends to be different
My dominicanidad's gender is the pink and orange sunset and smells like it does right before it rains

My dominicanidad hates the word dominicanidad
My dominicanidad isn't a token
instead she's glimmers like a gold coin in my pocket
Ready to be shown off when people ask "where are u from?"
My ambigous face with an obvious blackness people pretend they dont see
Act like you know
Act like you know

My dominicanidad grew up hating to be called morenita
And now wants nothing more than to reclaim that word as my own
Be coddled by it
so I never have to face my own face

My dominicanidad raises her hand first in class and walks out last
My dominicanidad loves post meal naps
And yelling back when im walking down the street
No tal ves otro dia papi no toy en ti
She loves hiding her fear behind her slick smacking lips

My dominicanidad loves playing under the sun and wants to raise her sons of here
But safe from here
Where no bacá will ever chase him

Where he can romanticize dominicanidad as colors and drums and plátanos and yellow fruits and summers spent fishing with his dad and all that stuff diaspora writers write about

My dominicanidad is wild and has been plunged under the sea
Where all the salt will cleanse her of all the curses she was born with.

The post had spread like wildfire.

No.

I'm going to start this part by saying that at the time this story got weird, the year was 2019 and my life had reached a new peak. I was supposed to be celebrating my debut novel which I'm going to call *Mamita* just to not be too on the nose with reality.

Mamita was a book about a young Dominican woman finding her footing in the U.S. after moving there when she was 15. Based on me.

I was doing my tour. Or "tourcito" as I called it because it didn't feel real. Because nothing in my life yet felt real. Because I was still in the air. I was still learning myself. And then.

The random ass attacks started. This fake page shared a real image of me with a t-shirt with a Haitian flag and began calling me a traidora.

Okay some context. As a Dominicana, I wore the t-shirt in solidarity with Haitian immigrants and Dominicans of Haitian descent who were being de-nationalized at the time in 2015. And it was also a nod to history, to how the Haitian Revolution eventually led to enslaved Black folks in the DR being freed. It was a nod to how Haitians have been involved in every part of our history, from the liberation of slaves to yes the very separation of Haiti and DR in 1844—like actual Haitians were also there for it. But, most Dominicans have been taught one main thing about their history, not how Colón invaded and raped Taínos. Not how Black folks were enslaved here via colonization. Not about resistance. Not about the civil wars or even the gringos invadting. But. BUT. They were taught (at worst) that Haitians enslaved Dominicans. And that being Dominican means celebrating first and foremost the separation from Haiti in 1844. So. A Dominican woman wearing a Haitian flag, this was seen as heresy or some shit.

At first, I ignored it. This shit had already happened before to any of us who had ever spoken up for the rights of Haitian immigrants and Dominicans of Haitian descent in the Dominican Republic.

The page had also moved on to share images of other folks in the Diaspora who had advocated for immigrant rights.

But then. For some weird ass reason. The post of my photo spread. Like wildfire.

There we go. Now a story is unfolding.

Okay. So this image of a young Dominican woman rocking a t-shirt with a Haitian flag began to spread. People were calling me a traidora. Saying that I was part of a group that was seeking to create a fusion between the DR and Haiti. And basically turning me and other activists into the face of this conspiracy theory that was meant to make people vote for the most right-wing candidate at the time—or some shit. Like our very own q-anon bs.

The image had been shared over a hundred times and other websites had gotten a hold of it.

The timing seemed so strange, because it had nothing to do with her book tour at the time. *Why did I change this to third person?* At least not at first. At first it was a coincidence. Because you see as soon as these folks found her page and realized she would be making a book tour stop in Santiago and Santo Domingo. Then, they really focused on her. On this book tour stop. On this person.

The flyer for her events in DR spread through the right wing underground spaces and a network of chats. Folks from the island she hadn't spoken to in years were texting her. A friend even told me it was being shared in her family chat in el Campo.

Like what the fuck. What the fuck what the fuck.

It was strange. she. I. She. Had gone viral but through a network that made it impossible to track it. So it wasn't really viral. But it was nonetheless very real.

Human rights groups reached out to her, advising her to cancel her tour.

The post with her photo spread, but also a quote of things she had said like how I believe el Día de la Restauración should be the actual independence day and not el 27 de Febrero.

This coupled with her photo, made it so that these groups shared her image as the face of the left wing ideals: THIS IS WHAT THE LEFT WANTS—TO VIOLATE OUR PATRIOTISM AND PATRIOTIC SYMBOLS. TO INVITE A HAITIAN INVASION.

And it's so weird to tell this story and to center my story because im an ally. but it was no longer about the fight or the message but about how me and others like me were being used as example for something larger.

She had to delete her Facebook account after someone shared it and dozens of these groups tried to access her information.

Then, one group started sharing the information about her book tour. *Wait did I already mention this?*

Okay maybe I did. But I'm tired. I hate telling this story. I'm telling it cuz it's important for this book. It's like a big part almost. Except I refuse to make it a big part. Except I wish it wasn't. Cuz fuck these people. So yes this part is ugly and messy. That way it's a footnote. That way maybe you skip it. Feel free to skip it. Yes. That. But also don't. Please don't. Please witness.

LOOK, THIS BITCH THINKS SHE CAN COME TO DOMINICAN REPUBLIC AND SELL HER BOOK. LETS SHOW HER WHAT SHE DESERVES they wrote.

One week before her trip, this was unfolding and she wondered if she should cancel or go.

She spoke with Julian *that's not his name*, laying in her bed wanting to literally die.

"What are you going to do?" he asked.

"I think I'm going to have to cancel," she said, showing him a comment where someone said they would throw feces at her, and someone else wrote, "We need to hire a crazy man to pegarle dos tiros."

Human rights groups and organizations had told her they cancelled events for the same reason. And she needed to cancel. But the folks in the space where she was holding it said she needed to host it. Stand her ground.

He had to work that night. And she thought of letting him go as she held on to her wrists. *They itched. Like they were begging to be opened. Like in that show on Netflix. 13 Reasons Why or something. She wanted to be like that teen girl. Found floating in the water in her tub. By her roommates.*

A deep sadness had fallen upon her, and she felt herself drowning in it. If he left, she knew, she wouldn't swim back up, she'd just fall in it, deeper and deeper.

All that work she had put into this tender book tour with her story. A sort of zenith in my life. She'd have to cancel her return to the DR. It's like they had won, they being the world, these groups, these people.

Anyway.

She felt worthless.

Then she remembered the life growing inside of her. And the work she had birthed before, the beauty. *Mamita* wasn't the only thing she could give this world. And she wasn't going to let it be her last. She had future characters to write into existence.

She had shit to do y'all.

“Please stay,” she asked him. Tears welling in her eyes like water bombs waiting to be detonated. “Please please call out of work please I can’t stay alone.”

She began falling and he caught her fall, sitting on the floor with her, holding her there by the door.

“Okay, I’ll stay,” He said.

Later that night. She told him. She wouldn’t cancel her tour. Because cancelling her tour and giving into this online harrassment would feel like letting them win. It would feel like losing something that had given her life for so long.

It would be like letting them kill her spirit.

At first I couldn't look them straight in the face. I didn't want to see it all. Like watching a scary movie. I only peaked through my párpados.

But eventually, I had to look. And not only look. I absorbed. I read. I read and re read and let myself dive into in their world like surrendering to a sinister rapture.

They were hollowed out humans, pretending to stand on two feet. Defenders of an ideology meant to keep them chained up like a dog that doesn't realize his leash is tied to nothing. And so he stays. He stays.

God's dogs.

It was right in my face all along. This is what it means to grow ravenous, spread rabies and let foam come out through your mouth, attempting to kill with a bite. The strength coming not from your jaw's grip but from the disease you spit.

Gods' dogs trying to tame this person they call their bitch.

denlen kilin por degrasi k es maltita
Esa gente lo que están provocando que le den un golpe, para darlo a conocer como racista.....
Pero qué se valla a promocionar su libro para República de Haití,que viene a buscar a RD si es enemiga nuestro país
yo estuviera en mi país hubiera ido con una botella de orina para tirarsela encima éso sí yo hubiera
aunque me llevarán presa
4 Replies
Recibamos a esa bruja cómo se merece
ba a comprar su asqueroso
Recibamos a esa bruja cómo se merece
que venga ,que le daremis un caluroso aplauso a esa desgraciada
Esa. Es no. Crata en. La Republica uno
traidora de la patria
QUI QUE NO VENGA A PRO
HAY QUE FUSILAR ESA
CROMAGNONA
193 Comments 171 Shares
Se merece ke le den un recibimiento a su altura...con huevo y tomate a ver si le da vergüenza y se
Ojala que aparez a un guapo que le de una buena carrera
z mardita idiota hay que hacer que se coma su
Pero se supone que hay patriotas en

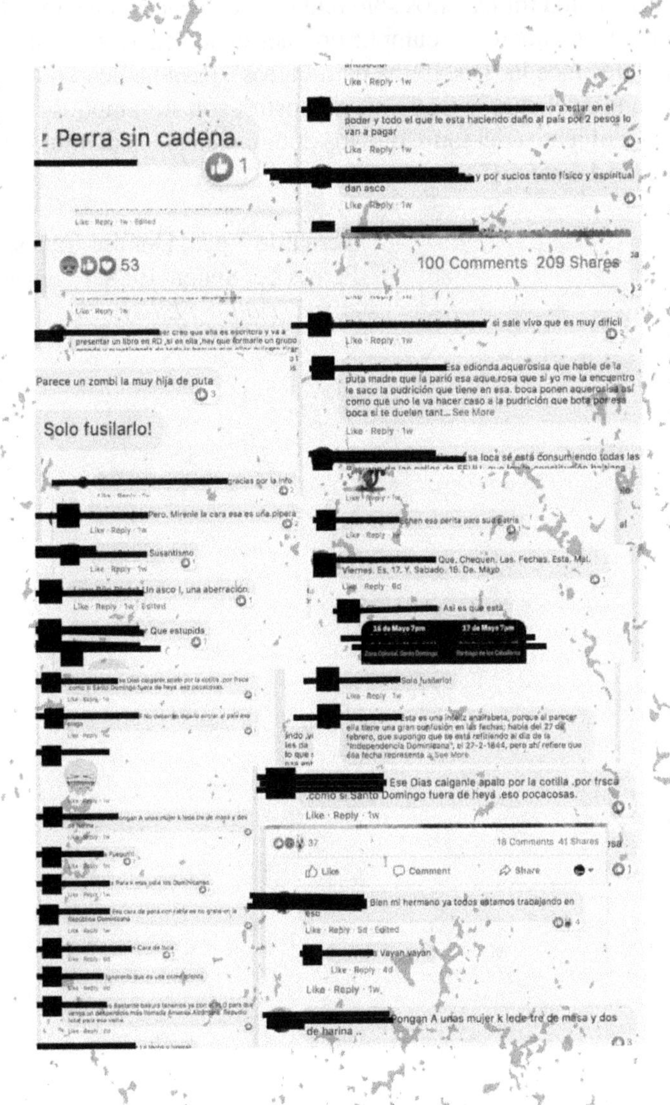

Perra sin cadena.
va a estar en el poder y todo el que le esta haciendo daño al país por 2 pesos lo van a pagar
y por sucios tanto físico y espiritual dan asco
53
100 Comments 209 Shares
si sale vivo que es muy difícil
Parece un zombi la muy hija de puta
Solo fusilarlo!
Esa edionda aquerosisa que hable de la puta madre que la parió esa aquerosa que si yo me la encuentro le saco la pudrición que tiene en esa. boca ponen aquerosisa así como que uno le va hacer caso a la pudrición que bota por esa boca si te duelen tant... See More
sa loca se está consumiendo todas las
gracias por la info
Pero. Mirenle la cara esa es una pipera
Susantismo
Un asco !, una aberración
Que. Chequen. Las. Fechas. Esta. Mal. Viernes. Es. 17. Y. Sabado. 18. De. Mayo
Asi es que está
Que estupida
16 de Mayo 7pm
17 de Mayo 7pm
Solo fusilarlo!
Ese Dias caiganle apalo por la cotilla .por frsca .como si Santo Domingo fuera de heya .eso pocacosas.
Like · Reply · 1w
37
18 Comments 41 Shares
Like
Comment
Share
Bien mi hermano ya todos estamos trabajando en eso
Vayan vayan
Pongan A unas mujer k lede tre de masa y dos de harina ..

“**En su** vida idílica ellos solo tenían que obedecer ciegamente, como cachorros falderos, y cumplir ordenes de nosotros, sus señores, los que establecimos la ‘Disciplina para Perros’. ¡Eso me lo explicó bien claro mi amigo el cura, cuando me demostró, con sus amplios conocimientos del latín, que los dominicanos, los domini canes, eran perros del señor!”

- Bernardo Vega, Domini Canes: Los Perros del Señor. 1988. *(Conversaciones entre Trujillo y Lilís)*

The domini-canes have fangs made from bones they collect in the dreams they disrupt. Some are made of milk from little girls who get smacked across the face when she plays with boys. When she wears skirts that are too short. When she talks back. When she smiles back. When he cries. When he's caught playing with dolls. When he wears make up. When she grows up and wears make up she buys with her own money.

The domini-canes' fur is spiky and clean like a porcupine but smells of concentrated perfume and beer breath that you've associated with your daddy and with home, so it's impossible not pet it, not to be lured by it, not to love it. Even if it hurts.

And when sugar cane workers ask for a pension, the domini-canes are there asking for papers. Or asking for proof, buckets of sweat don't count. While bullet-sized saliva spits out of their mouth, what is dignity when these stinky drops fall on human faces asking for their rights?

Domini-canes crack jokes when families ask for the gold from their land, ask for God to remember them while they prey on Rosarios. Domini-canes love white foreign perras and razas, and they don't call them cueros like the women here, instead they say they open like mariposas.

Domini-canes pray to la Virgen de la Altagracia and have built altars for her across the land like empty promises of love love love Mamita te construiré un castillo que llegue a la luna porque yo te quiero. I promise I won't hit you again. I promise. I won't hurt you again. Please wash my feet with your hair like you did when we first met. Please remember what San Lázaro said and let me lick your wounds.

WWJD

I feared very specific things like that they'd start hunting for me, with sticks lit on fire and shit. I feared/imagined/had nightmares that they'd begin a search across the country and I'd have to hide at a friend's place and then they'd find the friend's place and threaten to burn it down so I'd turn myself in and they would rip all of my clothes off and do all the things they said they'd do like throw shit on me and then they would burn me en la hoguera like they did witches. No, instead they would begin to rally around me and even though some friends would try to rescue me, they wouldn't be able to, the mob of people was strong and growing and growing and they'd tie me naked to this pole right in the middle of the street and they would put hay in the ground beneath me and douse me in gasoline and they'd light a stick with fire and before lighting me up they'd ask me if i had any last words and for some reason the words i remembered over and over again, the words that creeped up from my subconscious and I dont even know how the fuck it happened were "forgive them father, they know not what they do."

And there. That is when they'd light up the match. And i'd die. And it would be a release. A carrying out of this immense fear would liberate me from it. And this scenario would play in my head over and over again. And it'd stop me in my tracks. And I knew it wouldn't happen. Anxiety is so weird. I think. Get it over with. Surrender surrender surrender.

To come from women they call brujas means to not need validation
To know our power is not a figment of imagination
And our inner child is made of tender love not a crux
It means disrupting as a truth not as a burden
Havin fun while making potions
Crazy bitches don't u know it
God in my tongue healing erotions
Alchemist of the people
Our joy is our devotion

It means holding a legacy of light
In our darkest we are golden
In our blackness we are boldest
Fingers pointed, in your accusations against us
We are chosen

They chip away at us so we have to rebuild
Abuela's legacy in my memories
knitting a quilt

What will happen when I tap tap in
This aint just diamonds on my wrist
It's my aura light that flicks
Haters sick
Got the whole world in me all treats no tricks

I don't fly like in ur little books
But I rise like a rattle snake
Thick juice on my hips

U call me a risk but im the only one who can put out the flames with my lips
No te asuste
Im just showing u a glimpse

God
Make me into a painting
and place me in an obscure hallway in a museum
where only lonely art lovers go
and use the most vibrant shade of amber for my skin
and clear crystals for my irises
and hang me at the eye level of those whose souls are young and wise
and thirsty for life
so that I may be not immortal
but eternal
like a Sunday morning in the arms of a lover
so that my light may still shine
on humanity
and its despair
and its lost creatures
without making me its victim

In hindsight, maybe I should've canceled. Cuz a part of me did die when they protested my tour, when they interrupted me, when it felt like they turned this beautiful homecoming into a fearful moment, a human part of me left, and that's when I began transforming into a sea creature.

After the tour was over, I went on a getaway to the beach where i found myself paranoid, thinking every stare was someone who recognized me from a whatsapp conversation. "Mira esta traidora" they would read.

For the first time in my life, I hoped it was just men checking me out, approaching me to say hi. I knew how to ward them off.

Hola linda
Hola como esta
Tu y yo pegamos, he says with his yellow outfit
Sí, digo yo with my yellow bikini
Dejame ser tu novio, he says
Ya yo tengo novio

All his friends laugh
We're in the water, I'm surrounded by all of them. But i'm not even remotely afraid. I've learned to play along and decline with laughter.

Ella dice que tiene novio, an older man tells him
Siiii, pero cualquier cosa, si yo lo boto a el yo vengo a buscarte, i joke, as i swim away.

At the beach, I enjoy the things that make me proud of mi tierra.

The guy comes to get our orders. I described the fish that I want, to see if he remembers the name.

eso es filete de mero, no tenemos hoy, he said, *pero tenemos red snapper*.

I order it, con tostones y una fría. Shit was delicious. Nada mas una dominicana coño se come un pescado así, snapping the crunchy fins, sucking on the espinas, una experta. I forget to take a picture but we all know que esa vaina taba deliciosa.

My prima called my dad and left him a 13-minute voicenote. My dad sent it to me. I only heard bits of it, not the entire thing. It was a rant about how I'm being used to fusionar la isla.

My aunt's husband wrote a comment under a post my tía put of my book release. Saying something about Duarte and traidores paying for their crimes.

No one responded to him. Everyone just wrote their comments saying "congratulations" right below his. Me dicen que el casi se atreve a venir a protestar con los mismos nacionalistas.

Oh shit. I'm editing this and realizing I didn't tell y'all. So yes. The mother fuckers showed up to both book tour stops. In Santo Domingo, even the National Guard was there. Like what the fuck. I had to be escorted out of the building like I was some sort of rich famous person. A bitch is broke. I do not make enough money for this shit. In Santiago, they interrupted at the end of the event. Asking me questions during the Q and A about why I was at so and so event supporting so and so fusion conspiracy theory. At one point someone in the audience told me "Amanda you don't have to respond" and the event continued. Though I was exhausted af. Paranoid af. I went out with friends after to pretend all was good. LMAO. Even they looked at me like I was crazy. My friends actually thought the people interrupting were actors that I had hired.

These were the comments that hit home. The ones coming from family. The ones that made it harder to forget.

On our way home from the beach, we drive por la cumbre. This is where they disposed of las Hermanas Mirabal. I always remember this when we drive through here. There's no monument. Not even a cross. Just a school close by with their name like dozens of others across the country. But no reminder that this is where they died. Only oral history.

Sidenote, they've tried closing this road many times, saying people should drive por la autopista, but this thrilling road is really part of the experience.

My friend is una matatana, at 21 years old, she safely drove us, raining, through this road.

Once we begin to descend into the city, I spot a graffiti in a blank wall that says "fuera los haitianos." It seemed like someone had tried to block it by spraying an aerosol heart over it. It was a visual war.

Is this what it means to be Dominican?

a thing I *wrote after hosting the events in Santo Domingo and Santiago in 2019.*

Me dicen que esto demostró mi valentía
Pero no saben las horas que duré hablando del miedo que sentía
No saben como se me llenó la boca de agua cuando comencé a recitar mi poema
Como si el agua de todas las veces que me bañé en el mar, río, playa, laguna, pidiendo bendiciones
como si el agua bendita de cuando me bautizaron cuando era bebé saliese de mi en ese momento
Y estallará de mis labios
para hacerme un huracán
mientras recitaba mi poesía
“Nunca seré fina pero tampoco soy sencilla”
Sabiendo que estaba al lado de una ventana
Y que el poder tenía que venir desde las aguas mas profundas de mi ser
Porque si moría con ese vestido amarillo
De un balazo ahí mismo
O si me tiraban un tomate por la ventana
O una piedra
O pipí
O aceite
O mierda
O todas las barbaridades que dijeron que me iban a tirar
Tenía que por lo menos verme fuerte y buscar seguir
Volverme tormenta que aguanta y arrasa con todo
Nadie me quita mi verdad.

May 22 2019

I'm back in the US. and it feels like it did right after that time i spent two nights in a row in the ER. i'm feeling better. Like i can breathe deeper than i could before this all started.

And like my stomach and chest are empty, as if i had fasted for a few days.

I have felt this so many times. The morning after crying myself to sleep.

There's the calm before the storm. But there's also the quietness afterwards.

When el huracán Jorge came through in DR, when i was 7, i remember some of the storm itself, having to cover the windows, the mess of water that came in, sneaking into the marquesina to see how strong the winds actually were.

But what i remember most vividly is the aftermath. Sitting in the backseat as mami drove her light blue toyota camry around the neighborhood, then around all of santiago. We looked at the fallen trees, the flooded streets, the postes de luz that fell, the rumors of towns that are under water, el río yaque and how it rose all the way into the towns and up la subía where my grandfather once lived.

These streets are normally loud, with cars honking, motores with speakers strapped to the backseat.

That morning, not a single radio could be heard except for those announcing the news. Not a person spoke too loud, it was all whispers.

Silence. Space. Emptiness.

 yosoy_amanda •••

View insights Boost Post

yosoy_amanda I never talk about why I became a mermaid because so much of my unpublished upcoming body of work is about this, and I like grand entrances. But today I'll say, it's not about being pretty or about being looked at or about being perceived as a mythical creature that men lost at sea would take refuge in. It's about becoming a beast who learned to swim underwater so she wouldn't drown, who learned to cry out loud with a cracked voice. The irony is that now that I am re-emerging in two legs and that my conviction as a woman being grounded on earth is multiplied, is when I feel most mythical of all.

To my father, the man who was accused of touching a girl

Two years ago, i decided to stop talking to you. And then last year i suddenly started again. I started and stopped and started and stopped.

I told my therapist that i was afraid you'd suddenly die thinking that i didn't love you, but i did, and that's why this all hurts. She told me to send you a father's day card. So i did. I walked to the post office and sent it to you in the mail, and you responded with another letter begging me to talk to you again.

And it hurts because you're so good at giving advice. It hurts because at times you really feel like the only adult in my life who can speak to me and understand me, and who says things like "seek spirituality, not church, but spirituality," and advice that feels like secrets like "men like women who's next move they can't guess." It hurts because I recognize you in my charisma, in my spirit, and because i cant help but feel pride when i walk into the old neighborhood and they all say "esa e la hija de marco" like if I descend from barrio royalty, cuz everyone loves you so damn much. And it hurts because i wonder where did u learn this.

I became an uncommitted daughter who wanted to have her father in her life but who couldn't bear to be in his presence for more than a few minutes. And whenever we did hang out, you'd drink and I would drink and my brothers would drink and your friends' wives would drink, until the discomfort went away and we'd sing mariachi in decorated Pennsylvania basements.

And i come to you once in a while and fall in your arms and we pretend everything is okay. And i get on a bus and go to spend time with you and my brothers and bring my men to meet you and we pretend everything is okay. but nothing ever is.

And recently when ur brother died and I stood by your side during his funeral after we drank a corona on the way, I knew what it was like to be a daughter cuz it's the only time you ever showed yourself, your pain. You said, during his funeral, that you understood your little brother hid pain behind alcohol. Were you speaking of yourself? Of all the nights of alcohol and sugar under your tongue?

And I try to make sense of it all by letting go of the father figure, and remembering you too are a man. And with that, the magic cape falls and I see the wrinkles in your smile, the drinks on your hand even after doctors advice you no more. I hear the laughter as you become the life of the party. I see the sadness in your eyes.

and in my mind the question lingers.

Is it true, what she told me, is it true?

I couldve stopped myself. I know it.

But it's like the sea called me. When you swim, sometimes you think you're swimming in the ocean but it's really the ocean swimming on you.

After lyrics in "Hapi" by Spillage Village ft. Big Rube

Anyway tho.

Im not a victim but a survivor and a warrior
Una guerrera
And my people's climb can never be done in a single lifetime
So I been doing this for millennia
like an intergalactic Zelda

And so protected is my book of life
I can speak all this truth in this book
and still so much of me is only mine

All of me is only mine

I'm a spell u can't break
Armed with conviction and the strength of a thousand ancestors
They're all alive in my face

I'm an off-key piano
Going at my own pace
Played with soul
Guided by grace

Guided by grace

Y que suene la clave
Que abre el suelo in this place
Pa bailar
Que sin gracia ni gracias no se abre

No se abre

“For Carl Jung, the mermaid embodies an archetype that makes reference to the unconscious. The most prominent archetype that corresponds to the unconscious in Jungian thought is the sea. Based on the notion of the unconscious as the sea, Jung develops several interpretations of the mermaid archetype: he interprets the mermaid as an anima and as an alchemical metaphor that refers to the transformative structure of the unconscious and the process of coming to consciousness, known as individuation.

Playing on the notion of the mermaid as emblem of the transformative structure of the unconscious and figure of individuation, I suggest that the mermaid can be interpreted as the figure that traverses the oceanic realm of the unconscious. She is not stuck within in, as a neurotic is: her body, a hybrid of fish and human, has adapted to its watery conditions. She is part human, part Overhuman, in Nietzschean terms: she has overcome herself. In Jungian language, she has overcome the challenges and obstacles posed by the unconscious. In this sense, the process of navigating, and therefore overcoming the personal unconscious will be elucidated as a process of becoming-mermaid.”

- Cecilia Inkol, “Melusine Machine: The Metal Mermaids of Jung, Deleuze and Guattari”. York University, Toronto. 2018.

In the year 1532, in the Sierra de Bahoruco —a string of mountains filled with tectonic faults that are all connected— a man by the name of Sebastián Lemba Kalembo started a village of maroons.

It was a dark time, when white men enslaved entire populations in lands they stole, and entire people they stole from other lands, and in the process dehumanized themselves—opening a wound in this place first, on this island. On this Sierra. And unleashing a curse that would eventually spread pain across the entire world.

And somehow from that wound also came a resistance that manifested itself in songs that are called salves: salvation, potion for healing, song of the soul.

The village of cimarrones formed by Lemba was free. Free of pain and suffering. Or at least the suffering they had endured. Lemba and his men and the women who built with them, started a community while hiding and staying there until it was time to fight.

When they fought, they went from plantation to plantation: burning down the property of the white men who called themselves cristianos and called the men negros. And freeing all the enslaved people in these plantations. Until approximately 1547, when Lemba was killed in the south, and his head exhibited like a trophy.

And in these same mountains, men organized centuries later to fight against the Spaniards. And against men from the neighboring land. And in the early 1900s, against other men of the same land.

And in these mountains, men who called themselves mulatos also fought against the North Americans who called them slurs in English. Men in green coats who stole women and created a culture of buying girls.

And in this mountain range, decades later, a Black priest by the name of Liborio Mateo hid here too, forming an entire commune that also sang salves. Many called him el Mesías, during the time of a ruthless dictatorship that prohibited their healing songs.

From so much pain, so much cracking, an opening would be exposed close to where the earth stemming from this mountain meets the sea, revealing a blue flesh of the earth that had been hidden for millennia.

Kids would play with blue stones from this flesh by the beach, without a care in the world, before 1974 when the stone was "discovered" by a man named Miguel, and named Larimar after his daughter Larissa and the sea.

And mines would be dug by working hands, digging the stone in exchange for coins. Their flesh exploited. And the earth exploited. And everything around them exploited.

And the mountains. They remain. Until this day. And late at night. When no one is there to hear it. The leaves in the centuries-old trees sing a stirring song, free still. Grounded still. Creating a rhythm with drums still. And feet stomping the earth with their Black and Brown silhouettes still. And their hips gyrating with the wind still. And laughter between smiling teeth sucking on sugar cane stalks around an unlit fire still.

A lonely community of ghosts. Free. Free. Free.

And waiting for the next group of souls to come and join their dance with the moon.

“…**Pero no** pueden cortar el avance de la historia, no pueden cortar la lucha por los derechos de todas, TODAS las personas y no han podido nunca, NUNCA, detener la justicia social.”

- Inka, rapero y productor dominicano. Tweet luego de que censuraran su show durante la Feria del Libro 2022 por mostrar la bandera LGBTQ.

Somebody explain to me why my mind keeps going to the darkest of places after I keep showing it the light over and over again.
After I have to prove it wrong over and over again.

I think it likes it there. I think it has found a cozy spot there. A place of comfort there.

In expecting the worst, it feels safe. I feel safe.

And that's some tragic ass shit.

To feel safety in the darkest of places because that's what feels most like home.

***

This is how beasts are made.

***

You tell her to be quiet. To be small. To be nothing but beautiful. Like a porcelain doll picking a thorn from her toe with golden locs coming out of her head. And when she grows up to be what you consider the opposite of that. Loud. Angry. Imperfect. Proud. Black. Joyful. Free. Free. Free.

You will pretend not to see. How the world kisses the air she walks by. How breathtaking she is.

***

At least now I can see the downward spiral begin to form.

And I can see myself getting on the ride. Almost excited to join. Like yoooo I'm going home.

I'm going fucking home straight into the darkness that's always there waiting for me to return.

I tighten my buckle and try to tell myself to be gentle when I join the ride. The borrowed Xanny in my bedroom drawer screaming at me like a bad song stuck in my head on an endless loop.

But this ride is happening. And I don't want a sedative. I want to feel as it rips the scabs from the healing wounds off my skin with its speed.

And yet the spiral never lands as low as it used to. It never takes me back to that edge. Back to that blade..

And I want to think I miss the days when I could reach that low. But I don't. What I miss are the days when I wasn't building a new home for myself. The days when rest looked like letting the dirt in my house pile up. When rest looked like ignoring the sunlight instead of chasing it.

The days when I wasn't knocking down walls and putting up new ones.

Now on rest days I play music loudly and sing about la maldita primavera with it's shitty love cycle while I clean.

And I think.

I'm becoming like all the women in my family. Singing my heart out even if the neighbors can hear me. Cuz a bitch will always be loud af.

***

Maybe then. My question isn't why does my mind keep going to the darkest of places.

Maybe it's how can I learn to rest in a home that's under construction.

Escala A: Ansiedad: Muestra elevados sentimientos aprensivos o específicamente fóbicos, tensa, ind e inquieta y tiende a quejarse de una variedad de malestares físicos, como tensión, excesiva sudora dolores musculares indefinidos, nauseas. Muestra estado generalizado de tensión manifestado por incapacidad de relajación, movimientos nerviosos y rapidez para reaccionar y sorprenderse fácilme Se muestra notablemente excitada y tiene un sentido aprensivo de la inminencia de problemas, hipersensibilidad a cualquier ambiente, inquietud y susceptibilidad generalizada.

Escala D: neurosis depresiva (Distimia) alegría superficial, elevada. Las puntuaciones altas implican, aunque no parezcan en la vida cotidiana de la paciente se ha visto afectada por un periodo de dos o más años con sentimientos de desánimo o culpabilidad, una carencia de iniciativa y apatía en el comportamiento, baja autoestima y con frecuencia expresiones de inutilidad y comentarios autodesvalorativos. Durante los periodos de depresión, puede haber llantos, ideas suicidas, sentimientos pesimistas hacia el futuro, alejamiento social, apetito escaso o excesivas ganas de comer, agotamiento crónico, pobre concentración, pérdida marcada de interés paro actividades lúdicas y una disminución de la eficacia en cumplir tareas ordinarias y rutinarias de la vida.

VI. Conclusión

Relacionando los resultados de ambas pruebas se puede obtener un perfil de alto nivel de ansiedad propenso a conducta paranoide, neuroticidad y distimia. Se toma en cuenta características de su comportamiento en las relaciones interpersonales como castigadoras y evitativas que le impiden mantener relaciones a largo plazo.

Happy Father's Day to those of us who's dad are the abusers, rapists, child molesters.

To those of us who recognize him in our face and on our skin and our mannerisms and our smile, and still learned to love ourselves.

To those of us who tremble when we call him.

Because we know he doesn't deserve that shit.

But we do. Even if just to pretend for the little girl inside who still believes her dad is perfect.

Happy Father's Day to those of us who pretend to forgive even when he doesn't say sorry to the women he violated. Even when he doesn't acknowledge them.

Even when it feels empty as we wonder what does sorry mean in a world where there's no accountability. Even when it's so hard to reconcile it all.

Happy Father's Day to us because we know it's part of a cycle. And we know he doesn't deserve that shit. He doesn't deserve our forgiveness.

But we do.

That curse ends with us.

Does the curse really end with us if we're still talking to him though?

Nov 7 2021

I feel the emptiness today again. It's subtle but it's there. Today. Im trying to accept that this is life and ask for nothing more. Musings. Cuerpo colonizado. A veces me pregunto como vivo así.

Could emptiness be filled with something like softness. Soft caresses leaning on the tip of her tongue.

I miss when they hugged me. I miss their short hair and when they laughed at my jokes.

I miss them. I miss them. I miss them so much like the way you miss something u had to let go of then realize u never had.

Im a ball of anxiety there are days when my mind
It's like it's attacking itself
Valproic acid for mood swings
It's like a permanent acid trip except it's real life
Sometimes I miss art
Art.
  Art.
Art.

I have to take pills to drown out the emptiness. I wonder if this emptiness is why im susceptible to feeling the spirits, cuz im a vessel. Interesting how that works. Im an empath so im a vessel.

Those very beliefs could get me diagnosed as schizophrenic i think.

While taking the test, there were questions that made me think of my brother, and made me feel for him. Then there were some that i didn't realize i related to, that i wondered if others felt too

"Me estan siguiendo"

"Hay personas que me quieren hacer daño"

"Estan tramando algo contra mi"

"Estan hablando de mi"

This is all ptsd though. I think. I put no for some of these now but i know it wouldve been yes very recently. But i can see now how close i was to a psychotic break. Maybe i did have one. There were moments when i felt i was close to it. That fear drowning me.

I learned to swim i learned to swim

I'm not mad at these pills.

How can i be mad at something that makes me feel good, in a controlled way nonetheless.

I also feel myself on the edge of addiction though.

Like taking these drugs makes me want to drink more. The sadness is still there, beneath something. I think i drink to push. To sabotage.

All i want to is to get paid properly. And to be held properly. To be loved properly. I want to be held properly to be loved properly. Why is my brain falling apart this way.

It's ugly. I just want love and to be loved. I just want to be saved. Im floating right now that's how i feel woah i feel woozy.

I cant do this anymore.

What would planning my death look like.

Just consider it.

A letter.

The letter can be an end and a beginning.

A letter.

Maybe that is my destiny. Maybe that is how i take my power back.

Girl, stop.

It's just me and my drugs this week
And we have parties listening to john coltrane and Cuban jazz de ruben gonzalez
And we write love letters to ourselves and go to the beach that we visit on special afternoons when we feel like the male stares aren't daggers or worst, when we notice they don't care cuz in this whitewashed town de Cabarete, im a shadow. why did I move to cabarete? how did I end up here?

Is it bad to miss the attention even the bad kind cuz it's all we get?

Man, I don't care.

On nights like tonight, me and my drugs dance and my shadow twerks trying to make a hole inside of me and i push her out of her seat
I guess I'm a survivor
yes I've survived stuff stuff
yes you shadow are made out of a part of me that resulted from being cut open
yes I've suffered
yes I am sad mad woman
so what? let's dance.

Me and my drugs. They come in packs and have punch holes through aluminum and sometimes I push them out and worry they'll break but they never do. They never do they never do. I know you're jealous cause I filled this hole inside of me with synthetics but girl you were cutting me open trying to go back in and kill me. How can I integrate you without dying? We'll see, you mad woman

they say you're pretending to be mad, woman. I say my only desire, my only disease, is that I feel too much.

Did you ever hear the story of Maria La O? It's a song. If you stand by the ocean and say "Maria la o, Maria la o, tu Mamá es una puta y la mía no," Maria La O would make the ocean crash on you.

The story goes that Maria La O was a young girl with dark skin, black eyes and yellow hair. She was described as disobedient for talking back to her mom, the only person she had. She also didn't believe in the Church. One afternoon on Viernes Santo, she went to the river, even though only churchgoers were allowed to go this day. And when she bathed, her swimming became light, almost instinctual. That's when she saw that the bottom half of her body had become fish-like. When she got taken out of the river, her body didn't change back. So she had to live in this river forever. Here, Maria La O started crying, crying so much that her tears gave way for the river to rise and connect to the sea.

This story is told as a cautionary tale. But all I can think about babygirl, is that Maria La O was finally free.

*Source: MITOS Y LEYENDAS DOMINICANAS. 11 de julio de 2013. Author unknown. buenastareas.com/ensayos/Mitos-y-Leyendas-Dominicanas/31292920.html. 1 de Mayo de 2022.

Social death means I already dont exist

la muerte que nos espera significa que ya fui cancelada

como que ya el tipo aquel me dejó asesinada

como cuando se cayó el techo de mi casa pero el lease ni a mi nombre estaba

era invisible, muñeca sin cara

y el súper dijo ‘que pena que no te cayó encima mientras dormías

porque hubieses sacado tremenda demanda’

Quizás me abro la piel pa sentir algo en esta necrópolis, a veces no siento nada

> *“Yo soy de P fuckin' R, R*
> *Donde yo crecí la vida no vale na'*
> *So, mejor que no te aferre', -ferre'” – Arcángel*

Built a backbone
out of clavo dulce:
Each threat a hammer to nail
Each side eye a threaded needle
Each tooth
collected in dreams
a vertebra.
Height of 33 feet
a monument
to all the women in me.

At the edge of the earth. Humans used to think that we would fall. Because the naked eye could only see so far. And when you look out into the ocean, it makes sense.

And it is hypnotizing. And it looks empty.

What happens when a whole nation is born out of that emptiness? Then if you're not careful. Men, abusive men, leaders, will come and say "I am your father" and give that empty child empty love.

Down under, in the core of the earth, where our subconscious lies still, is a human with a fetus we call woman who's feet are actually roots feeding the core.

She's crying all the time, and across the world, myths of women crying exist reflecting her. She's crying for her babies that were ripped off her hands and raised by wolves.

Her burning desire, stemming from her chest, from her pain, feeds the core of the earth. It keeps us here. Her tears flood the oceans.

She has stretch marks from where her belly once stretched. Wailing into the evening. For centuries.

The sea waves moves back and forth with her breathing. And when we throw our pain into it, and our garbage and our residues, her pain just grows. But she still loves us. Still feeds us. Cuz we are her kids.

Maybe it's love that fuels her. Love and pain and love.

And she loves the land. But she has no nation.

Sometimes i want to die. A lot of times actually. I know I won't, at least not in a suicidal way. So this isn't a cry for help. It's just a truth.

When I go surfing every morning, I have to face wave after wave smacking me in the face as I dive in, trying to get far from the shore so that I can catch a good wave.

I'm still learning. So I have to stay here, in the area called "white water" because it's where the bigger waves break, to catch their ripples.

And every morning, the biggest wave of all seems to be the one I bring with me: the voices in my head. Showing up as worries and to-do lists for the day. Showing up as hurt.

I can feel the torrent of emotions broiling inside of me like a tornado trying to find its way out. When it is met with the ongoing doubt whenever I fall from the board, or whenever I fail to catch a wave, it finally finds its exit in salt coming from my eyes.

Lately, whenever I'm failing, I pray, I pray to the sea like maybe it'll calm down for me. And I always learn the only way it'll calm down for me, is if I quiet the storm that I come with.

It's not the sea that's a tsunami, it's me.

And I'm constantly reminded, it's not the waves that need to be good, it's I who have to will myself to stand on that board, to follow all the steps. Cuz the waves keep coming, I know it, because they smack me across the face over and over again, like incremental wake up calls.

A whole metaphor for life.

Today, I stayed a little longer than my usual hour and a half. And I tried something different. Instead of praying to God for patience, and to help me overcoming my storm, for some reason, I prayed to my grandma.

At the same time, in another part of this island, I later found out her tomb was being exhumed and her body was being moved. I wonder if this is why I thought of her.

A few days ago, I went in the water filled with worries again. With anxiety.

I thought maybe the water would clear this.

Instead. The opposite happened. The storm in me was too much to handle, and to make matters worst, the water was pushing everyone to the same direction—you see the waves always go in one direction, pushing everyone the same way. But this day there were stronger.

And I ended up by folks from an old surfing school where I started learning. Being in that space was embarrassing for me. I took so many classes last year, and after making some progress, it's like I got worst. I didn't want my old instructor to see me. I was dying of shame and embarrassment.

And in the middle of the storm brewing inside of me. this dude who kept hitting on me over and over, and who I've constantly rejected, decides to swim past me, while staring straight at me, and singing a love song. I looked the other day, pretending I didn't see him, as he "parked" waiting for a wave almost right next to me.

At that point, all my insecurities just flooded over me. I was struggling to learn, to catch waves, to surrender to the moment. And I recognize now that I was being ridiculously hard on myself. But back then I couldn't think of that. Then, in the middle of battling my own insecurities to learn this sport, in comes this motherfucker to torment me.

I pretended not to care. In my head.

But of course I did. I was angry at being a woman. And how this is supposed to be one of those spaces that feel far from all that, and instead here's this motherfucker.

I swam out. Hoping a wave would catch me and help my swim to shore. That didn't happen. I just swam out with my arms dragging me. Defeated.

I dropped my board off by where my new instructor leaves his stuff. He wasn't there. Everyone was in the water, except for this one gringo australiano who was far away.

And there, I stopped fighting back tears and just let them swim out of me.

I walked out more and went further to the area where no one goes, to sit and cry.

This happens a lot. Me crying while surfing. It's happened while in the middle of a class.

"Tengo que llorar ahora, solo te lo estoy avisando," and Robbie who was teaching me would laugh, saying I get so angry at myself it's funny.

This new instructor, when I stopped us in the middle of class the next day because i had to cry, all he said was we're all facing our own thing, so he understood.

That day when I was defeated and stepped away to cry, before arriving home, I stopped at the super market and bought as many American snacks and comfort foods from the store as I could muster. Snack pack chocolate pudding. Goldfish. Oreos. Tostitos with salsa.

I went home. And in that moment, surrounded by snacks, I realized that I had tried to do so many things right, and what I hadn't done is accepted that the emotions in me were happening and it's ok. it's ok to feel them.

I was shaming myself for feeling.

And I was rejecting myself. And in my rejection, I felt rejected by everyone somehow. Like the whole world had turned against me. Like I wasn't deserving of any love, or friendship, or sisterhood, or warmth.

But. in acknowledging the hurt I was causing myself, in acknowledging my emotions, in acknowledging that it's ok to learn something new, I felt part of me return to my body.

Like my body was safe again. Like. I was home again. It was very strange and beautiful. A beautiful thing. To be back.

I had somehow created a safe space for my inner child to return and it was amazing.

I wish I could explain how momentous that was. To return to my body like that. Like part of my soul came back.

In allowing myself to feel the hurt, instead of pushing it away, it's like the storm was able to calm down because there were no contradicting feelings anymore.

My therapist says I run from emotions because it's what I've learned to do.

When I returned to the water. After days of feeling like a failure. I was patient with myself. The insecurities were still there. And I thought of dying again. Cuz I didn't want to feel. But it was okay. I wasn't going to run away.

In DR riding waves not dicks
Still looking like I caught a lick
The world at my finger tips
What's love in a town that looks
Like a bad flick
Beautiful women
Take ur pick
Everybody chasing brick
I'm chasing risks
Quit my job to chase words
Tongue a sword
They call me hick
Cuz I talk slick
Cuz I say malas palabras like wanting my body
Don't make u sick
Yea take a pic
if u just chasing something quick
Im not ur chick
I leave u dripping juice so thick
Now careful u don't blink
When I'm swerving on that surfboard
Don't u wish u were the atlantic

When I went surfing the last time.

The sadness that I felt, it shocked me. Just the depths of it. But I also felt a tinge of joy because I knew that I was going to get help.

I had an appointment with a new therapist.

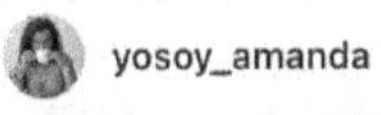
yosoy_amanda ...

yosoy_amanda To call myself something out of this world is to define myself for myself. At least that's how the path to freedom began. Cuz they'd want me to shrink. To become small. Fed me dreams in spoonfuls of sugar and hydrochloride and told me that was the remedy I needed to breathe as the weight of the world fell on my lungs. Never forget, I am light. Light as in weightless energy that can still run the world, even with no feet.

.

.

.

Gracias a @franchesca.ssosa por este hermoso dibujo inspirado en mi homenaje a las sirenas—mi hermana sirena y galáctica y con un vision que también está fuera de este mundo 🌍

I started writing a book about you. I named you Karisley, my granddaughter. About how you'd live in a society that aspired to be utopic, to give back land, to become sustainable, to heal the earth, to heal our wounds. It was a future only achieved after so much suffering, after millions of deaths from hurricanes and tsunamis and wars.

And you'd come back to DR, where your ancestors were from, after finding a map in a riddle that I had written for you. You'd come via boat. And you'd fulfill this prophecy.

The riddle said that in a magical land where the wound of the new world began, after driving by a street where metals moved backwards, and after you'd find an abandoned museum named after a foreign priest who used plants to heal, you would land in a city where the famous Cassandra was born. South of that, where the earth cracked open to pave way for the ocean, was a healing stone that would lead you to the beginning of civilization, the stone of Atlantis.

Around 1910, the sleeping prophet, Edgar Cayce, said that in the 1960s or 70s this stone would be named.

And you'd go on this journey, out to prove to your mother that your grandmother was alive under the sea and this stone would get you to her.

But instead, when you went, you found a dirty stream coming out of the mouth of the mines where the stone used to live, like a purge.

And when you touched the water, you had a dream of a woman wailing with stretch marks in her belly. And she told you that your grandmother was safe, away from this world that ripped babies off mothers' hands.

And when you asked her what happened to the magical stone, she told you that your trip there was never about searching or finding a thing. It was about the journey. And in that journey, you didn't have to heal anyone or save a whole community or the whole world. You only had to learn to love yourself.

And with that, your ancestor who created you would be happy because it meant they had survived too.

"The dream of you kept your ancestors alive," she said.

Freedom for me has looked like cutting my hair and getting a nose piercing and opening a bookstore and leaving jobs that wanted to put me in a box and ignoring so much shit. And it sounds so simple I promise you I know it does. But the transformation within was intense.

A few years ago, when I was doing research in Dajabón interviewing women to learn about their lives on the border of DR and Haiti, I joined a group of activists, organizers, journalists, and church volunteers to Pedernales, on the southern border. Because the international road that runs through the border from north to south was deemed too dangerous for a group of folks on a bus, we went the long route which required going through the entire country from Dajabón, through Santiago to Santo Domingo, then across the south through Barahona to get to Pedernales. We were truly triangulating the island.

Anyway, I'm just sharing that part cuz the journey was incredible. But it really is not important to my point. The part I wanna get to was when these girls asked me about my tattoos. They were 14-15 years old and they asked me "y tu novio te deja tener tatuajes?"

Recently I cut my hair, and while I've been struggling to feel cute, I also enjoy the way it cut down my prep time, and how bouncy it feels against my cheeks. I like that it makes it harder to hide my face. It makes me feel exposed in a way that at times boosts my confidence because it makes me love me for me. And at times it makes me want to hide. I was talking to my mom, via Facetime, showing her that I'd dyed my hair blonde. And she told me, "I think you should let your hair finally grow again, es que ese es tu encanto, así te consigues un novio."

That's the mentality I grew up in. Everything is meant to be for men for men for men. Nothing more nothing less.

In my culture, by going to college, I became less marriageable. By getting tattoos I became less marriageable. By getting a nose piercing, I became less marriageable.

And I would be lying if I didn't admit it's annoying until I realized, more than a husband, what I want, for real for real, is a baby. A baby. A child to call my own. To love and to hold till death do us part. Or till they grow up to hate me and move out and then I'll have my bff's and old ladies from yoga class and vecinas and widowers and lovers and brujas to be my bff's while I watch my kid make a life of their own that I'll tell them I'm proud of, as long as they're happy and healthy and not hurting anyone. (I gotta have some standards o sea).

Anyway, I lost my point.

My point is. Becoming free has required giving up everything i thought i needed to be. It has meant relearning a new way of being. I want to say it's like a butterfly spreading her wings for the first time after being told she had to stay a caterpillar, but no.

It's more like having lived by water my whole life, and yet always feeling like it was too cold. And it hurt. It was uncomfortable. So I hugged myself and my teeth shattered, and my chest compressed as I tried to retain all the warmth I have. Then. I realized. The answer isn't to hold the heat inside like a last lifeline of warmth and love, even though it's what I was told. Even though it was my initial instinct. The answer instead is to open my arms, and let my body feel the temperature. Let the water reach my chest and armpits and every nook in my body. Let it get accustomed. And let myself become one with the water. And then swim freely.

Like I belong.

For the women who are silent about their abuse

I know what it's like to have
The pain of what happened grip you tight
Like a leather belt with its edges worn out
And once it's unbuckled
There's nothing to hold you so
you unravel and feel
l i k e w a t e r
constantly
F
 a
l l i n
g
And you build a deep well for your pain
And cope by
adorning to it with gold edges and rose petals
And whispering tenderly into it
And comforting it by saying "i'm strong because i survived this"
And carrying it within the depths of your soul
And letting it become an endless source of empathy

My wish for you is that you always find your way to the sea
With its endless darkness
Holding all of the world's deepest secrets
And release

Take 2

It's just me and my drugs tonight
And we dance to John Coltrane
And Cuban jazz
And we pretend to smoke un cigarro with a pen in our mouths
And ignore the blue ink at the edge of our lips
And my drugs make silhouettes of joy out of my hips
And make me cackle out loud deeply like
Digging a laugh out of a pit
I wonder if the neighbors can hear me
I wonder if im la loca de la cuadra
Me and my drugs are blessed
And because of them I no longer see death on my doorstep
Instead I feel an energy in my chest
like synthetic spirits made in a lab by white men in white coats
And the ingredients got names I can't pronounce
And I love them love them love them
Let's dance like no one is watching
Mamita, no one is
Except all my ghosts
Saying come dance with me

How I Became a Mermaid

The scales on my skin itched like fucking crazy. They formed a soft blue pattern that I couldn't look away from as I stared into the mirror, mesmerized by the colors, even though the transformation was slowly destroying me.

It started on the subway the day before, on the A train on my way to 125th St in Harlem, close to where I worked. The train ride was only 20 minutes, sometimes less, from Washington Heights, but in this one train ride so much happened. It's like time stopped.

I had an itching coming from my chest and my neck that had started the night before. It felt like something was biting me from the inside. I took a Zyrtec to try to calm it down, and drank some ginger tea, grinding the ginger before pouring it in the water, letting the juice get between my nails, like I'd seen elders do.

Before leaving the house, I did had a small hive on my neck area...but I ignored it.

As I sat on the train that morning, I couldn't ignore it anymore. The itching suddenly became unbearable. I scratched my neck. Got up and squeezed through some people to stare in the reflection by the doors. I was red all over. A teen kid noticed me scratching, and quickly walked away.

"Ew, you got chinchas, get away from me," the young teen said, looking up from his phone with disgust.

Others turned to look, and scrambled to get away, quietly. Staring.

I couldn't stop scratching, uncontrollably, all over my body. It was as if I had red ants crawing all over me. I forgot where I was, and started scratching all over my arms, taking off my coat, dropping it on the floor. People started to more intentionally walk away and step back, while still staring straight at me.

Then, my throat closed off, and I folded over my stomach, wheezing, trying to catch my breath. And yo, I swear I almost saw my breath leaving me, slowly, like a transparent floating ball of stardust and sparkly neutrons lifted out of my mouth. A lady in a bright pink nurse uniform quickly pushed through the crowd.

"Get away everyone, she's having an allergic reaction," she said. "Can you breathe at all?" she asked, staring straight at me, putting her hand over my chest.

I could only stare into her eyes, but I was unable to find my voice. I wasn't breathing, but I wasn't fainting either. It's like I could just kneel there, not breathing, in a stillness that felt lifeless but till awake, forever. Is this how mummies felt? Surrounded in gold, wrapped in cloths, waiting for their breath of life to come back?

The nurse put her ear against my chest, confused. "You're not breathing, but how…how are you sitting up? Are you ok?"

There, her voice reminded me of something I had in my bag. My purse was on the floor. I looked down, unzipped it in a daze, and began looking inside of it frantically, finally realizing I should be terrified that I wasn't breathing.

The nurse, with her thick fingers covered in rings, quickly noticed I was looking, and stuck her hand in, helping me search. In the bottom, it was her who found it. My asthma pump. She held the back of my neck, put the pump in my mouth and pushed down. I breathed in. And the steroids kicked in, waking my lungs back up, like doing chest compressions. She did it again, and this time I was able to inhale harder.

And just like that, I was breathing again. Everyone stared. I finally found my voice.

"I'm okay. I'm okay," I said. I grabbed the nurse's soft hands, they reminded me of my older sister's. "Thank you."

Everyone was relieved. Someone who had started recording seemed disappointed that nothing more exciting had happened.

The entire episode must've been less than a few minutes because it all happened in the time between 168th st and 125th st when the train goes express.

I got up as the subway door opened, and I walked out. The nurse kept staring at me. In her eyes, I saw curiosity, like she knew something was up.

When I got into the office, I felt disheveled, but tried to move past the whole thing. Everyone was talking about a pandemic that started in China and had began to spread in Europe.

I just walked into the bathroom to check out my neck and saw nothing, then I began unbuttoning my shirt and saw my skin was turning blue. But, it wasn't a bruised blue. Instead, it was shiny and translucent, and if I looked close enough, I could see my veins, my lungs, even my heart.

What the fuck.

I walked out of the bathroom, still ignoring it, because I refused to go to the hospital for asthma again. I had just been in the emergency room the week before, and already owed money from shit the insurance didn't cover. Nah. Hospital wouldn't fix this.

I walked back into the office, cleaning off the dust from my knees, ready for the day. I felt okey. Sort of.

Hi, it's me again. I know, I know, this was interesting but, this time I'm part of the story and not just here to interrupt it.

You see, in this part, cleaning the dust off my knees reminded me of La Chiflera, the song that Fefita infamously sings the best that says, "a toda la mujer chiflera, se le jincha la rodilla." I'm assuming the song is tryna say, her knees become swollen from sucking a man's dick.

And then it got me to thinking about how one time I was sucking on a guy, and wanted to stop because I wasn't enjoying it. And I didn't like him anymore. And I told him I was tired and wanted to go home. And he forced me to finish.

And how the last man I was in a situationship with, he was an asshole too. And sometimes I get embarrassed thinking about how I let him treat me so badly. I get so embarrased, I don't even talk about the stuff he put me through yet. Someone who wasn't even claiming me publicly. When I think about him, I want to disappear.

This was somebody I was with at 30 years old! Like this shit is not supposed to be happening to me anymore. I'm not supposed to be putting up with rapey shit like waking up with a dick inside of me after I said no.

What I'm proud of though, is that while at times I felt that I was losing my dignity, I didn't kneel for him. It's like I kept that to myself since that day.

I will only kneel for Dios herself.

I told myself that, as I composed myself that day. Like, this was my life, just moving with this shit. Until I couldn't anymore. Until that day when I said fuck all.

When I got back to my room that day, *in the apartment I shared with strangers from Craigslist,* that's when my chest began to literally break apart, like my lungs were transforming, making it so that I didn't feel dead when my breath left me. Instead, I welcomed the lack of air.

This whole breaking generational curses shit is hard as fuck.

Like, why do I have to know all the family secrets? Is it because I'm born to write, and I'm supposed to share them with the world? Is it cuz I'm supposed to keep record of them like some sort of trauma archive? "Oh and Titi Carla was abandoned when she was seven."

A thick purple mucus engulfed all of my lungs and my back cracked, making my spine thin and more flexible. It hurt like crazy, as if someone was smoothing out my back with a rasp.

I think I first broke a curse when I broke up with the dude who put it inside of me in my sleep. The dude who would yell at me when he came over and food wasn't ready.

And I think I broke it when I started facing the dark parts of me instead of looking away. When I started accepting I'm not perfect and that's ok.

I stared into the mirror as the sun began rising on that hot summer day and I was barely human. My eyes looked white, my skin was translucent all over, and my feet were loosing muscle strength.

The dark truth is a part of me felt that I deserved that shit that homeboy had put me through. That I deserved to be treated like a dirty bitch who deserved to be spoken down to.

The dark truth is, another part of me enjoyed it. And that's the biggest confession of all: Another part of me liked it because I assumed on some learned behavior shit from when I was a kid and almost only got attention when something was wrong, that maybe, ha! maybe if I am a victim, maybe if I am hurting, maybe if I am being hurt. Someone will come save me. Maybe if I say "I am being abused" someone will feel sorry for me, and hold me tight and cradle me to sleep like a baby. And take care of me. Maybe pity can be how I fill the emptiness that's been bubbling up. Maybe that's how I heal the abandonment.

And it was some sad backwards thinking shit cuz no one ever comes to save you.

I saved myself. I ended a cycle by walking away. By choosing me over and over again.

My vagina also began turning inside out, a wet sticky liquid oozing out of it, giving me an in-measurable pleasure, creating a web between my thighs and calves, trying to bond my feet, but I kept cutting the web with my hands. Hoping more and more of the juice would ooze out of me. How could this transformation be so pleasurable and painful at the same time?

Have you ever felt a tenderness when you touch a certain bone in your body that often goes ignored? Like when you push down on your elbow, when you massage the bone on your thighs. That heaviness in your shoulders that you seem to have been born with.

I truly believe that that thing. That tender pain. Is inherited from the trauma our ancestors went through.

And I wanted to heal from that pain.

So, I left him. And I left them. And took time to rest.

I cut the emotional cord from the voices in this world that kept telling me I wasn't enough. And I made a potion of ginger and onions and malagueta and agua bendita that rid me of the binding belief that I deserved pain.

And I learned to receive a love that wasn't attached to pity. That wasn't attached to my own demise.

Love that water gives me. The kind of love that I feel when I'm floating and I know, the ocean is the womb that birthed me. Maybe that's Yemayá. Letting me embrace her feet like a child playing under a dancer's wide skirt.

Maybe it's the wildness of my brain and its faulty mood regulation and serotonin receptors being tangled up.

I got quickly dressed up as best I could once the sun was fully out. I wore dark glasses and a hoodie, and a long skirt. It made no sense for the cold weather of that day to wear a skirt, but I was trying my best.

My legs felt like jell-o as I walked out of my place on 175th, down the block to Forth Washington, and up towards the George Washington Bridge. The strength was leaving my legs with every step, but I tried.

My brain felt more agile, maybe because now it wasn't preoccupied with breathing anymore.

I arrived and began walking across the George Washington bridge.

I think, I think healing isn't about becoming more human, or more normal, or even learning to be functional in this backwards society. It isn't about being productive as fuck. I think it's about leaning into the wild, whatever that means to each person. Without harming others of course. And without harming yourself of course.

I love my wild. I love all of me. And I deserve the best. Even if it means imma stay unmarried like why the fuck do they place so much emphasis on that? Even if it means I might never be able to hold a 9-5 job. Even if it means, some nights I want to dance like fucking crazy with red wine stains on my lips, blowing the roof off my house and jetting into the sky. Even if it means, some nights I have to be gentler with myself and be okay with crying under the shower like a fairy living in a land made of concrete.

To me healing is leaning into the shit they call crazy. It's allowing myself to be delusional. To believe what isn't real while remaining grounded in my truth. While remaining grounded in love.

And I'm here thinking, with all of that in mind, how can I give my character love? And the question comes up again, am I supposed to keep the character in this book alive? Am I supposed to keep her here? Why, when she's had so much to bear? Why not set her free?

She can have that. She can be more than human. She can be free and real.

There, the netting seemed impossible to get through. Authorities have fixed this bridge to prevent this. But I had strong ass arms now, so climbing felt easier than normal.

And I, I wasn't going to die though. This was different. I was here for a different reason than the others who had jumped. I was going to live.

Outta nowhere, a young woman tried to stop me. She got off her bike almost falling, and threw it to the side.

Then she ran towards me, stopping when she saw my blue arms holding the ropes, my legs now connected in one big wet mass of scales under the skirt. And she took a step back, covering her mouth in shock. I looked back at her and showed her my white eyes, my fresh fangs, she got scared and ran, screaming.

I had reached the other side of the net now, and was hanging, staring into the traffic. I looked at the cars that began to stop close to me, at the human faces, one last time. I turned and looked into the city. Its greyness. Its hardness. Its magnetic energy field attracting millions.

Then, I gazed down, to the Hudson River under me. I thought of the coldness in its depths. Of the souls that must roam it. I wonder if I'll meet other creatures like me. Away from the nations. The cities. The labels. A place where I was whole.

And in that moment, I let go of the ropes, and began to fall.

Letter from the author

Lately, I keep wanting to write futures for us. And presents where I can live. Untethered to symbols that wish to eradicate me. Able to choose. A mermaid, a shapeshifting fairy, or a myth. Reimagining what it all could look like. Like Octavia Butler whose futures were unbound by convention. Futures where Black and Brown people create communes amid the chaos. Where a time traveler liberates her lineage from the cruelty of slavery. Where a religion like Earthseed based on change and chaos exists cuz maybe that's all we've known.

And sometimes I wonder if fictional worlds are maybe the only place where we can be free, the only place where we can experience magic, since so many of our heroes of all kinds often met untimely deaths and assassinations. Mamá Tingó. Las Hermanas Mirabal. Lemba Calembo. Maria Olof. Liborio Mateo.

But then. Then I ask, how dare I assume they weren't ever free? Or that they didn't experience magic? They had magic all along. And perhaps the greatest proof of that is that we have their stories. They made us remember.

Our own lives are magical too, but so often we fail to see that. The magic lurks in every chance encounter, in every soothing cup of tea, in every morning breath. Like a ceremony, we move in the circle of our lives trying to make sense of what does it even mean to be here. And since 2019, for me, being here has been about this book and the transformation at the center of it—becoming a mermaid and surviving my own brain. Yet once I was at the other side of the transformation, at the other side of finding a way of surviving the horror of humanity, I found myself feeling more human than ever, and realizing being human is about accepting the beast in us, and loving it. Showing it love and tenderness. Showing it and each other grace and forgiveness.

And reminding myself I deserve joy and I deserve to live. And please know, so do you.

At the other side of publishing this book, I also feel so liberated from the weight of the task to tell this story. Unlike my past book *Chula,* this collection here was not always fun. There were nights of dancing when I felt free as I wrote, when I was having a blast. Then there were nights when I wrote for me, in order to keep me here, and never thought those words would ever make it into a book. Yet so many of them did. And I'm so grateful for that. Because though writing this story was difficult, the process kept me alive and going. It gave me hope and purpose when things were confusing. And it felt like medicine. The kind that tastes bitter but that destroys bacteria along the way.

Though these words are rough and at times also bitter, I crafted them with love, magic, and devotion. And I hope this book is medicine for you too.

***

For this story. This piece. This book. This thing here that I birthed. And the performance accompanying it on social media. I want to thank all the people around me who helped. People who held my hand as I pushed.

First, God. Thank you. I'm so grateful for everything. Thank you too to my ancestors. My spirit guides. My abuelita. Mis abuelitas y abuelitos. The plants and ancient fire who guide me. That air that I breath. The ground that I live in. The sea that holds me.

My family past and present because con todo y todo, what you share is what you've been taught. My mom. Mami. I love you. And kinda hope you never read this cuz I think you won't really get it. You'll be like oh my God la ropa sucia no se lava en público. and I understand that emotion. I do. My sister. You are a star. I love you. To my madrina Dionis, you don't know how much you've given me. Thank you. I love you. To my dad, eres mi amigo y te quiero, aunque a veces sea dificil—y esa es mi verdad. A mi otro padre Bernabel, gracias por apoyar mi loquera, por siempre estar ahí. Te quiero.

Thank you to someone I met recently who has become a close friend and confidant and who told me it would be selfish not to publish this. Laura Peña. Te quiero tanto amiga, hermana. Gracias for being there and for listening to me talk about this for months. And thank you for taking the photos/videos that would help announce this book. You were a doula for this book.

Thank you to my cousin Sara García, you know. You fucking know. I gotchu you always, forever. I'm so grateful to you for being there for me. Thank you to Moraima Capellán for being a cheerleader, for saying yes to helping with photos and anything I needed. For inspiring me to take action. To Sara Surani, I miss you—thanks for being such a great listener.

Gracias a Freco, por decirme que publicara eta vaina y ya, como el hace con su graffiti. Gracias a SK por pintarme como sirena y hacer mi sueño realidad. To Eddaviel, this fucking cover is breathtaking, rompiste. Gracias.

Gracias a mi psiquiatra, el Dr. Carlos Dominguez, who is the best and never makes me feel like I'm crazy or weird. Gracias por dejarme ser una paciente díficil que no cree en las pastillas, y por responder a todas mis preguntas con claridad. Gracias por hacerme sentir que estoy en confianza. Gracias por enseñarme a tener paciencia conmigo misma.

To the therapists I've had throughout the years, you've held my hand when I needed it most. Thank you for helping me make sense of it all.

To my community in Cabarete, I love you even when I don't always understand you. To my friends in NYC and across the globe, I love you and miss you dearly. To my fellow artist friends ¡Seguimos! I love you.

To Angy Abreu and Dominican Writers, you have done so much for me and for us, thank you for always supporting my work. To the Brujas of Brooklyn and the community I met through the sadhanas you hosted, I'm so grateful for our journey in sisterhood.

To my detractors, the mean ones, the ones who send threats and try to instill fear, the ones who call me names, the ones who protest in person, the ones close to home. You are but the fruits harvested on this hurting land. And, for coming for me, I forgive you.

Artist's statement

I am a Caribbean palabrera living in Spanglish. A wordsmith making a name for herself between two worlds, using the written-word and theatrical performance as tools to confront a society that tells me to be less. That is less loud, less outspoken, less sexy, less black, less immigrant, less visible, less me.

With my writing, I declare myself a puta and a feminist, and let myself be free via the pen. Beyond the binaries that confine us, challenging the pressure to be monolingual or nationalist in both the United States and the Dominican Republic. Challenging the pressure to conform to society's standards of womanhood. With each essay, I surrender a story to the world, and make my existence permanent amid constant social death. As a working-class woman of color, change is the only constant in my life, as is nostalgia. So I write as if the sun is always setting, with pain for what's lost, and hope for what's to come.

With each poem, written boldly con flow, I embrace the Spanish from the country that raised me, the same one that others say is not good enough. Because we cut the esses, and the r's, and have invented a new language.

And they say I make space for Dominicans, for women of color, for people like us, like me.

But with my words, I don't merely make space. I build homes, ones where I exist fully, without folding.

Mi casa. Palabrera.

Printed in the USA
CPSIA information can be obtained
at www.ICGtesting.com
LVHW021515121123
763715LV00046B/897

9 780578 294452